DISNEY PRINCESS

POCAHONTAS

Book Seven

DISNEP PRESS
New York • Los Angeles

ong ago, there lived an Indian princess named Pocahontas. She and her friends, Meeko the raccoon and Flit the hummingbird, loved adventure.

Her father, Chief Powhatan, believed that it was time for her to settle down. "Even the wild mountain stream must someday join the big river," he declared.

But to Pocahontas, rivers were always changing. They weren't settled at all.

Confused, Pocahontas went to see Grandmother Willow, a wise and magical tree deep in the forest. She told the tree about her father, and about a dream she'd been having: "There is an arrow before me that spins until, suddenly, it stops."

Grandmother Willow smiled warmly at Pocahontas. "It seems to me this spinning arrow is pointing you down your path," she said.

Just then, a breeze blew through Grandmother Willow, rustling her leaves. The wind was speaking to Pocahontas.

Pocahontas climbed into the tree's branches, trying to hear the wind more clearly. Looking out over the trees, she saw strange clouds in the distance. Suddenly, she realized that they weren't clouds at all. They were the sails of a great ship!

The ship was the *Susan Constant*. It had sailed all the way
from England. On board were settlers in search of gold. A man
named John Smith jumped off the ship first. As he made his
way through the forest, Pocahontas couldn't help following.
She had never seen anyone with such pale skin and yellow
hair before.

John Smith stopped by a river to take a drink. Suddenly, he saw Pocahontas's reflection. She started to run, but he called out to her. "Wait! I'm not going to hurt you!"

John Smith smiled and held out his hand. Just then, a breeze swirled up around them. Listen to the spirits . . . Pocahontas reminded herself. Taking his hand, she smiled back.

Soon, the two were talking. John Smith told Pocahontas all about London, the city he was from. "We'll build one like it right here!" he said.

Taking John Smith by the hand, Pocahontas showed him the beauty of her land. Slowly, Smith realized that it was his people who had much to learn.

The next day Pocahontas snuck off into the forest to meet
John Smith. Her father had warned her that the new settlers
were dangerous, but Pocahontas didn't care. She led him to
Grandmother Willow, who startled Smith by greeting him.
Soon, they were chatting like old familiar friends.

Later, Pocahontas spoke with Grandmother Willow. "I
know I shouldn't see him," she said. "But something inside is
telling me it's the right thing."

Grandmother Willow thought for a moment. "Perhaps it's
your dream," she said at last. "It appears, my dear, that you
have found your path."

When Pocahontas returned to her village, she found the men preparing to fight.

"We don't have to fight the settlers!" she told her father. "There must be a better path."

Pocahontas knew she had to make John Smith speak to her father. She was sure the two could find a way to make peace.

Pocahontas's friend, Nakoma, tried to stop her. But
Pocahontas wouldn't listen. "I know what I'm doing," she said.

Worried, Nakoma begged a warrior named Kocoum to
follow Pocahontas. When Kocoum saw Smith, he attacked
him. A settler who had followed Smith jumped out and shot
Kocoum. Suddenly, more warriors appeared. Thinking Smith
had killed Kacoum, they captured him.

Back in the village, Pocahontas's father sentenced John Smith to die at dawn.

"I'm sorry," Pocahontas told him, brokenhearted. "It would have been better if we'd never met."

"No," he said. "I had to meet you. If I'd never known you, I would have no idea how precious life can be."

Sadly, Pocahontas went to see Grandmother Willow.

Just then Meeko handed her John Smith's compass.

Pocahontas watched the tiny arrow spin around.

"It's the arrow from your dream!" Grandmother Willow said.

The arrow stopped and pointed toward the rising sun.

"You know your path, child," said Grandmother Willow.

"Now follow it!"

Pocahontas raced back to the village. "If you kill him, you'll have to kill me, too," she told her father.

Suddenly, the settlers burst out of the forest. They raised their muskets, prepared to fight for Smith.

"Look around you, Father," Pocahontas told Powhatan. "This is where the path of hatred has brought us."

The great chief listened to his daughter. "Release the prisoner," he said.

The warriors lowered their weapons. But the greedy leader of the settlers, Governor Ratcliffe, had no interest in making peace. He grabbed a gun and fired it at the chief.

"No!" John Smith cried, pushing Powhatan out of the way. The bullet hit him instead, and he fell to the ground. Furious, the settlers grabbed the governor and locked him up on the ship.

John Smith was alive, but his wound was deep. "He'll die if he stays here," the settlers told Pocahontas.

Pocahontas gave Smith a small pouch of medicine. "It's from Grandmother Willow's bark," she said. "It will help with the pain."

Her father laid his own cloak over Smith's body. "You are always welcome among my people," he declared.

Smith begged Pocahontas to go to England with him, but
Pocahontas could not say yes. Her path, she knew, was with her
own people.

"But I can't leave you!" said John Smith.

"You never will," Pocahontas told him. "No matter what
happens, I'll always be with you. Forever," she promised.